D0903634

GYLES BRANDRETH

BRAIN-TEASERS AND MIND-BENDERS

Illustrated by Ann Axworthy

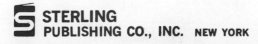

STERLING
PUBLISHING CO., INC. NEW YORK

Other Books by Gyles Brandreth

A Joke-A-Day Book
The Biggest Tongue Twister Book
in the World

Copyright © 1979 by Sterling Publishing Co., Inc.
Two Park Avenue, New York, N. Y. 10016
Original edition published in 1977 under the title "Brain
Teasers and Mind Benders" by Carousel Books, a division
of Transworld Publishers Ltd., text copyright © 1977 by
Gyles Brandreth, illustration copyright © 1977 by Trans-
world Publishers Ltd.
Manufactured in the United States of America
All rights reserved
Library of Congress Catalog Card No.: 78-66297
Sterling ISBN 0-8069-4596-6-Trade
4597-4-Library

CONTENTS

J
793.7
B
copy 1

5.6.0
BTPB
10/2/75

INTRODUCTION

If you took a very large piece of ordinary writing paper and cut it in half, and then cut the halves in half, and then cut the quarters in half, and then cut the eighths in half, and went on repeating the operation fifty-two times, and if when you'd finished you stacked up all the pieces of paper you had cut, you would end up with a pile of paper over 150,000,000 miles high.

Believe it or not, that's a fact. The mind boggles, doesn't it? At least, *my* mind boggles. And if your mind boggles too, then I think this is a book you're going to enjoy, because I have simply filled it with puzzles and problems and posers and pastimes that have baffled me, and I'm hoping they're ones that will baffle you as well.

I have a small brain (it was pea-sized according to my last math teacher) but it loves to be teased. There's almost nothing that it and I enjoy more than pitting our wits against some hard, knotty puzzle and coming up with the right answer. Of course, we have our good days and our bad days. On the best of our good days the brain and I can even tackle the three-star teasers. They are the really difficult ones and you will find them in the book marked like this:

On the worst of our bad days, I'm ashamed to say we even find the one-star teasers tough going. They are supposed to be the easy ones and you will find them in the book marked like this:

And on the days in between the good and the bad we take a look at the two-star teasers. They are the not-so-easy-but-not-so-tough ones that you will find in the book marked like this:

My brain and I have had a glorious time testing all the teasers and we only hope that you and yours will have as much fun trying them.

GYLES BRANDRETH

1. For Starters

Put the twelve boxes into the right order and what do you get?

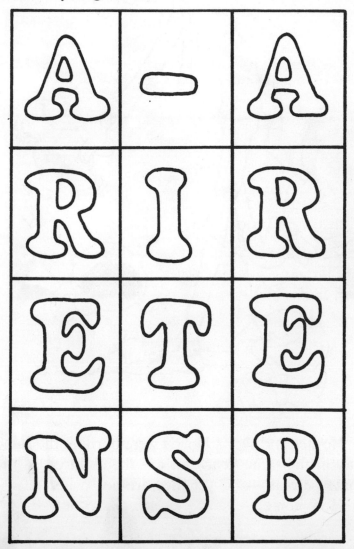

2. Twin Twister

Horace and Doris Norris were born on the same day in the same year and are the children of the same parents—and yet they are not twins.

How come?

3. Letter Salad

Here are five lines of letters:

```
I C A C
I C A B
I C A J
I C A U
I C A Z
```

One of the lines doesn't belong to the series. Which one?

4. Equal Division

Once there was a very wise king who was approaching his 79th birthday. He had two sons, and he wanted to be sure that when he died they would not quarrel over the division of his property. But he knew that it was not enough to write in his will that the property should be divided equally.

What did the king say in his will to ensure that both sons would feel that the property was equally divided?

5. Please Translate

"A slight inclination of the cranium is as adequate as a spasmodic movement of one optic to an equine quadruped utterly devoid of any visionary capacity."

What did you say?

6. Ninety-Nine Not Out

Find a number whose double exceeds its half by 99.

7. A Time Teaser

When you see the reflection of a clock in a mirror and the time appears to be 2:30, what time is it really?

8. Odd Man Out

Of course, all the little men on the opposite page look odd, but, believe it or not, one of them is even odder than the rest. Which is the little man who doesn't fit into the series—and why?

11

9. Alarming

If on the last day of February 1976—and re-member, 1976 was a Leap Year—you had gone to bed at seven o'clock, having set your alarm clock to wake you up at 8:15 in the morning, how much sleep would you have had?

10. Scrambled Eggs

Here are ten sentences that don't make sense. Unscramble the words correctly and you can make them make sense. If you manage to do it in ten minutes, you're intelligent. If you manage to do it in five, you're super-intelligent.

1. eggs eggs I to boiled prefer scrambled
2. brain trouble with no A brainy has teasers tough brain
3. day Always to a twice your you brush teeth tooth want decay if avoid
4. mythical extinct a The the and beast is dinosaur is unicorn
5. foolish five say mistake to fifty To times a is is make that five
6. city is as windy known the Chicago

7. John the first on was not Glenn moon man the

8. his fool and soon money A parted are

9. The a a is is an an and creature that small cross like between anteater armadillo aardvark

10. men women the the All a and and merely world's stage players

11. Surprise Your Eyes

Which of the two center circles is the larger?

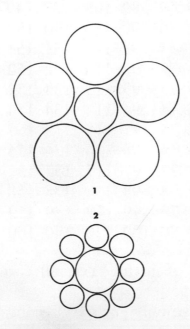

12. Sixty-Second Countdown

Here are two
hundred numbers:

1	21	41	61	81	101	121	141	161	181
2	22	42	62	82	102	122	142	162	182
3	23	43	63	83	103	123	143	163	183
4	24	44	64	84	104	124	144	164	184
5	25	45	65	85	105	125	145	165	185
6	26	46	66	86	106	126	146	166	186
7	27	47	67	87	107	127	147	167	187
8	28	48	68	88	108	128	148	168	188
9	29	49	69	89	109	129	149	169	189
10	30	50	70	90	110	130	150	170	190
11	31	51	71	91	111	131	151	171	191
12	32	52	72	92	112	132	152	172	192
13	33	53	73	93	113	133	153	173	193
14	34	54	74	94	114	134	154	174	194
15	35	55	75	95	115	135	155	175	195
16	36	56	76	96	116	136	156	176	196
17	37	57	77	97	117	137	157	177	197
18	38	58	78	98	118	138	158	178	198
19	39	59	79	99	119	139	159	179	199
20	40	60	80	100	120	140	160	180	200

Now add them up. Yes, all two hundred of
them.

And you've only got sixty seconds to do it in!

13. The Missing Letter

Here is a puzzle that's easy to work out if you do it with pencil and paper, but almost impossible if you try it without—so try it without.

Think of all the letters of the alphabet.
Now take away the second.
Now take away the twenty-second.
Now take away the one that comes before the last one you took away.
Now take away the letter O and the letter that comes after the letter that comes after O.
Now take away the sixth, fifth and fourth letters.
Now take away X, Y and Z.
Now take away the third letter.
Now add Q.
Now take away T.
Now take away the seventh letter.
Now add the last letter.
Now take away H and the letter that comes seven places before it.
Now take away the letter that comes before R.
Now add the letter that follows P.
Now take away R and P.

Now take away the remaining vowel.
Now take away the three letters that follow it.
Now take away N and the letter that comes before it.
Now take away the last letter of the alphabet.
Now take away the consonants in the word "sew."
What are you left with?

14. What's What?

Here are twenty questions that aren't as simple as they sound.

1. What is it that no one wishes to have, but no one wishes to lose?
2. What is always coming, but never really arrives?
3. What is it that you can't hold for half an hour, even though it's lighter than a feather?
4. What is it that's put on the table, cut and passed, but never eaten?
5. What is it that occurs four times in every week, twice in every month, but only once in a year?
6. What is full of holes, but still holds water?

7. What is the one thing you break when you name it?

8. What is always in front of you, even though you can never see it?

9. What is plowed but never planted?

10. What always weighs the same, whatever its size?

11. What is large enough to hold a pig and yet small enough to hold in your hand?

12. What is it that the person who makes it doesn't need, the person who buys it doesn't use for himself and the person who uses it does so without knowing it?

13. What is it that everyone, no matter how careful, always overlooks?

14. What can be right, but never wrong?
15. What exists on its own substance, but dies the moment it has devoured itself?
16. What is it that has no length, no breadth, no thickness, but when it is given to you you definitely feel?
17. What is bought by the yard, but worn out by the foot?
18. What will always be down however high up it is?
19. What goes from New York to Philadelphia without moving?
20. With what could you fill a barrel to make it lighter than when it is empty?

15. Santa's Socks

In his cozy little igloo near the North Pole Santa Claus keeps a large chest of drawers. It is made of pine and is a very handsome piece. It has six drawers, and in the bottom of those six drawers Santa keeps his socks. Santa Claus has cold feet so he needs a lot of socks. He has thirty-six socks in all, and eighteen of them are red and eighteen of them are green.

Since it's very dark at the North Pole, Santa

Claus can never see what he's doing, so when
he opens his bottom drawer to fish out a pair of
socks he isn't able to tell which color he has
picked. To make sure of having one matching
pair of socks, how many socks must Santa take
out of his bottom drawer?

And to be certain of having nine matching
pairs, how many socks must Santa take out of
the drawer?

16. Next Number, Please

In each of these series what should the next number be?

1. 31 28 31 30 —
2. 3 6 12 24 —
3. 1 9 0 1 2 0 0 —
4. 2 3 5 9 17 33 —
5. 5 5 25 8 8 64 3 3 —
6. 1 12 1 1 1 2 1 3 —
7. 1 6 2 7 3 8 4 —
8. 940 839 738 637 —
9. 4 8 32 512 131072 —
10. 111.11111 125 142.85714
    166.66666 200 —

17. Looking Ahead

There is a year in the not too distant future that when divided by 2, and the result is turned upside down and divided by 3, and that result is left as it is and divided by 2, and *that* result is turned upside down, gives an answer of 191.

What is the year in question?

20

18. One Word

There is one everyday English word which, when printed in capital letters, reads exactly the same upside down as it does the right way up.

What's the word?

19. Spooner's Spoonerisms

It was William Archibald Spooner who created the Spoonerism. He didn't do so on purpose, of course. He just happened to be the sort of person who gets a bit muddled now and again and jumbles things up without meaning to. He told off one of his laziest students with these words: "Sir, you have hissed all my mystery lectures and tasted the whole worm." Naturally, he meant to say, "Sir, you have missed all my history lectures and wasted the whole term," but that's not quite how it came out.

Can you translate these Spoonerisms?

1. If you don't hurry you will miss the bass lust.
2. I have just received a blushing crow.
3. Who colled kick Robin?
4. There's nothing like a lood gunch of haggs and esh.

5. What dall we shoe with a shrunken dailor?
6. Who missed ky Kate mate is mill a stystery.
7. The little log daft to fee such sun and the cow mumped over the June.
8. We mish you a Werry Christmas and a Nappy Yew Hear.
9. It's park in the dark after nix at sight.
10. This is a pilly garty same if ever pi layed one.

20. Ling Ting Wan Faw Su

Ling Ting Wan Faw Su was Chinese, but he lived in Japan. He worked for the Tokyo Tea Towel Company and spent most of his time writing the words "Made in Japan" on the bottom left-hand corner of his firm's famous tea-towels.

Ling Ting Wan Faw Su worked on the twenty-ninth floor of the Tokyo Tea Towel Tower, the enormous skyscraper that his company owned right in the heart of Japan's capital city. Every morning when he arrived for work Ling Ting Wan Faw Su would take the elevator to the nineteenth floor, get out of the elevator and walk up the remaining ten flights of stairs. But in the evenings he would get into the elevator on the twenty-ninth floor and travel all the way down to street level in the elevator.

Ling Ting Wan Faw Su was a very fit man and had no need for extra exercise, so why did he walk up those ten flights of stairs every morning?

21. Tall Tale

Here are four matchstick men walking up the street. Which of the four is the tallest?

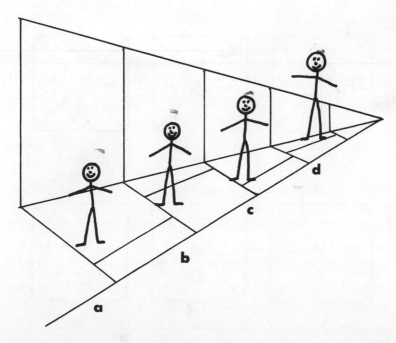

22. All the Signs

Here are nine squares and inside each of the nine squares you will find a plus sign, a minus sign, a multiplication sign and a division sign.

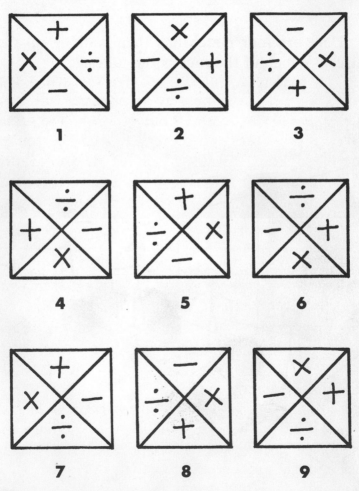

There is something rather different about one of the nine squares. Which one? And what is it?

23. Crazy Quiz

Here's a crazy quiz for the quick-witted. Give yourself just five minutes to answer all ten questions. If you score 10 out of 10, you're some kind of genius. If you score 7 out of 10, you're pretty bright. If you score 5 out of 10, you're sort of average. If you score 3 or less, well, never mind. There are plenty more quizzes to try. Good luck!

1. Folk is spelled F,O,L,K, *not* F,O,K,E. Joke is spelled J,O,K,E *not* J,O,L,K. How do you spell the white of an egg?
2. How many grooves are there on a phonograph record that revolves at 45 r.p.m. And how many are there on one that revolves at 33⅓ r.p.m.?
3. Mr. Broke the Banker has two coins in his left-hand pocket. Together they add up to 75¢. One of them is not a quarter, so what are the two coins?

4. What do you find right in the middle of Minneapolis?

5. What one word in the Oxford English Dictionary do people from Chicago always pronounce incorrectly?

6. In a Leap Year, how many months have 28 days?

7. What do you get if you add 2 to 200 four times?

8. If I have 467 large whatsits and 193 small whatsits in my prize whatsit collection and I take away all but a dozen of them, how many will I have?

9. In the whole history of the world, have New Year's Eve and New Year's Day ever fallen in the same year?

10. I own something round and flat and black and shiny with a small hole right in the middle of it. Is this a record?

24. One Number

If you add 1,000 to a certain whole number, the result will be actually more than if you multiplied that number by 1,000!

What's the number?

25. Unlucky Thirteen

Here are thirteen letters:

J F M A M R J J A S O N D

One of them doesn't belong to the series. Which one?

26. Loony Letters

1. Why is the letter A like 12 noon?
2. What comes after the letter B in the alphabet?
3. Why does the letter C make people feel ill on board ship?
4. Why is the letter D like a wedding ceremony?
5. Why is the letter E like death?
6. Why is the letter F like Paris?
7. Why is the letter G like midnight?
8. Why is the letter H so helpful to the deaf?
9. Why is the letter I like a broken leg in the Alps?
10. Why is the letter J like a noisy bird?
11. Why is the letter K like a roast pig's tail?

12. Why is the letter L like a tired elf with a twisted ankle?
13. Why should you never put the letter M into the freezer compartment of your refrigerator?
14. Why is the letter N like a pig?
15. Why is the letter O like a well-kept home?
16. Why will the letter P help a donkey who is taking an exam?
17. Why is the letter Q like your best friend?
18. Why can't you have friends without the letter R?
19. Why does the letter S frighten the top of the milk?
20. Why is the letter T like Easter?
21. Why is U the jolliest letter of the alphabet?

22. Why is your nose like the V in Vivian?
23. Why is the letter W like a flirty pen?
24. Why is the letter X like a permanent invalid?
25. Why is the letter Y like the wasteful child of a generous father?
26. Why is the letter Z like the letter T?

27. Wonder Word

There is a word which, according to the dictionary, means "metrical movement determined by various relations of long and short or accented and unaccented syllables."

It's an amazing word, because it contains six letters and not one of them is A, E, I, O or U.

What's the word?

28. Homeroom 102

There were nine boys (Ralph, Robert, Ronald, Billy, Burt, Barry, Carl, Charlie, Chris) and three girls (Gloria, Grace, Gale) in Homeroom 102 at the Florence Nightingale Junior High in the fall of 1972. They were a nice group, noted for their good manners and friendly ways. They were also very generous.

In fact, so generous were they that at the beginning of term they all decided to share their pocket money equally. Every boy in Homeroom 102 gave an equal sum to every girl in Homeroom 102 and every girl gave another equal sum to every boy. That done, they all had exactly the same amount of money.

What was the smallest amount of money that each of them had when they had shared it all?

29. Two to Go

Can you supply the two letters that are missing from this series?

A R - - I T E C T C E T I H C R A

30. Card Sharp

There are three playing cards lying in a row:
 A diamond is on the left of a spade—
  though not necessarily next to it
 An Eight is on the right of a King
 A Ten is on the left of a heart
 A heart is on the left of a spade
What are the three cards?

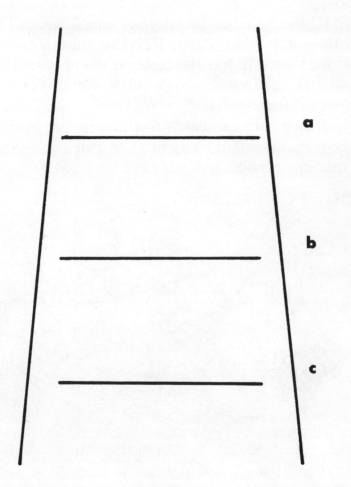

Which is the longest of the three lines—a, b or c?

32. Cats Catch Rats

If you managed to get your tongue around the title—and "Cats Catch Rats" is quite a tongue-twister—see if you can manage to get your brain around the puzzle—and "Cats Catch Rats" is quite a brain-twister!

If five cats can catch five rats in five minutes, how many cats do you need to catch a hundred rats in one hundred minutes?

33. The Two Bricklayers

Two bricklayers are going for a swim. One bricklayer is the father of the other bricklayer's son.

How are the two bricklayers related?

34. Triangular Challenge

Take a close look at this drawing:

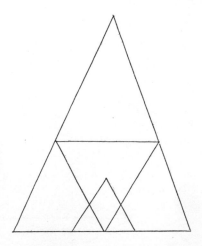

Now on a separate sheet of paper try to draw the diagram WITHOUT LIFTING YOUR PENCIL OFF THE PAPER AND WITHOUT CROSSING OVER THE LINE YOU HAVE ALREADY DRAWN!

35. Seven Numbers

Which of these seven numbers doesn't belong to the group—and why?

21 35 14 49 28 70 60

36. The Longer Line

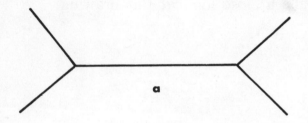

a

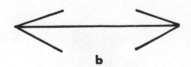

b

Without using a ruler, can you tell which of the two lines is the longer one? Is it a or b?

37. New Haven Bound

Wild Willy McDonald is traveling on the nine o'clock express train from New York to New Haven. As the train passes through Stamford it is traveling at 93 miles per hour. At that point, Wild Willy, who is standing in the aisle, jumps three feet straight up in the air. Where does he land?

38. What's Missing

Can you supply the sign that's missing from this series?

39. What Comes Next?

1 5 10 20 50 100 500 —

40. What's This?

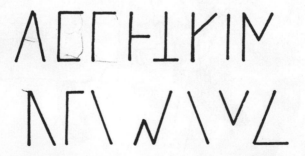

Well, what is it?

41. Family Reunion

"I gave a little party for the family last night," said Fred proudly.

"How many people did you invite?" asked Phil politely.

"Oh, not many—just two fathers
  two mothers
  one grandmother
  three grandchildren
  two sons
  two daughters
  one brother
  two sisters
  one father-in-law
  one mother-in-law
  one daughter-in-law
  and four children
    —that's all."

"That's all!? I make that twenty-two people!"

"Twenty-two people! Don't be ridiculous. There were only seven of us altogether."

How come?

42. Ask a Silly Question

Well, why not? The last few puzzles have been pretty puzzling, so if you feel like sitting back with something simpler, now's your chance. All the questions on this page are fairly silly—but not half as silly as the answers!

1. What does a girl need for brushing her teeth, combing her hair and keeping the rain off?
2. What do you lose every time you stand up?
3. What should you always try to keep, since nobody else really wants it?
4. What occurs once in a minute, twice in a moment, but not at all in a split second?
5. What do you look into every day?
6. What always comes at the end of everything?
7. What is hard to beat?
8. What stays hot longest in the refrigerator?
9. What smells most in a pig-sty?
10. What gets wetter the more it dries?
11. What can you break without hitting or dropping?

43. What's Next?

In each of these series, what should the next letter be?

1. B C D G J O P Q R S —
2. A C E G I K M O Q S —
3. B B B S H Y A W Y S —
4. T E B A H P L A E H —
5. A B F G K L P Q U V —

6. B C D F G H J K L —
7. T B M T B M S H T R —
8. C F I L O R U X A D —
9. G Y L E S B R A N D —

44. Think Big

Here are three simple-looking brain-teasers with quite surprising answers. If you come up with anything like the right solution for any one of them, you're no fool.

1. If an ordinary fly were enlarged 1,000,000,000 times, how large would it be?
Would it be:
> as large as an orange?
> as large as a house?
> as large as Mount Everest?
> as large as the moon?

2. If you laid $250,000,000,000 worth of pennies in a single line, how far would that line stretch?
Would it stretch:
> from New York to Boston and back again?
> from Washington, D.C. to Seattle, Washington and back again?
> right around the Earth twice?
> from the Earth to Mars and back again three times?

3. If you took a chess-board and placed one grain of sand on the first square, two on the second, four on the third, eight on the fourth, sixteen on the fifth, thirty-two on the sixth and kept on doubling the quantity on each square, how high do you think the pile of sand would be on the last square?

Would it be as high:
      as a milk bottle?
      as a sandcastle?
      as a two-story house?
      as a mountain?

45. Pick a Pint

With nothing at hand except a three-pint jug and a five-pint jug, how can you measure out exactly one pint of water?

46. Lost Letter

There's a letter missing in this series:

    J I K H — G M

Can you find it?

47. Dotty

Take a sheet of paper and draw twelve dots, like this:

Without taking your pencil off the page you can connect all twelve dots with six lines, like this:

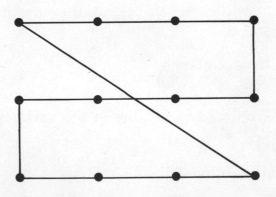

Or like this:

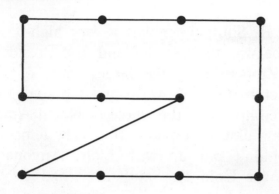

But can you connect all twelve dots with only five straight lines? Remember, you mustn't lift your pencil off the page.

48. A Comedy of Errors

Their are three misteaks in this sentence. Can you spot them?

49. Poor Miss Gump

Enid R. Shutheimer was a very high-powered lady. She was the founder and first President of Zappy Zippers Inc., the largest firm of zipper manufacturers in the world and the sixth largest private company in the whole of North America. She was a clever woman with a fiery temper and she wouldn't put up with fools. Anyone who worked for Enid R. Shutheimer had to be as bright as a button and as zippy as a Zappy Zipper.

Anyone who wasn't bright and zippy, got the "pink slip"—which is why poor Miss Gloria Gump, Enid R. Shutheimer's new English secretary, happened to be fired on her very first day at work! Poor Miss Gump, she meant well, but she simply didn't have what it takes. In fact, Enid R. Shutheimer fired her secretary after hearing her answer the telephone once and once only. The telephone rang. Miss Gump picked it up and a voice said: "Can I speak to Enid R. Shutheimer, please?"

MISS GUMP: Who's calling, please?

THE VOICE: My name's Harp.

MISS GUMP: I beg your pardon, sir, can you spell that for me?

44

THE VOICE: Harp. H for Horse, A for Ape, R for Rhinoceros—

MISS GUMP: R for what, sir?

THE VOICE: R for Rhinoceros, P for Panda.

MISS GUMP: Oh, Harp. Thank you, sir. I'll just put you through.

From that conversation, how could Enid R. Shutheimer tell that Miss Gump was a fool?

50. Nutty Numbers

1. Why is two times ten like two times eleven?
2. If two's company and three's a crowd, what are four and five?
3. What odd number when it loses its head becomes even?
4. Why do nice people, who have been well brought up, never use the number 288?
5. From what number can you take away half and leave nothing?
6. What is the difference between 100 and 1,000?
7. How many times can the number 41 be subtracted from 822?
8. When a sentry faints on duty, what number must you take to him?
9. When do 1 and 1 make more than 2?
10. What's the difference between six dozen dozen and a half dozen dozen?

51. A Problem of Parallels

Some of the twelve horizontal lines on the next page are quite straight and parallel with one another. Which ones?

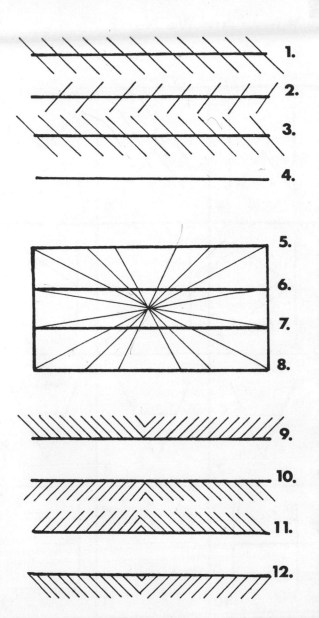

1.

2.

3.

4.

5.

6.

7.

8.

9.

10.

11.

12.

47

52. Where Are We Now?

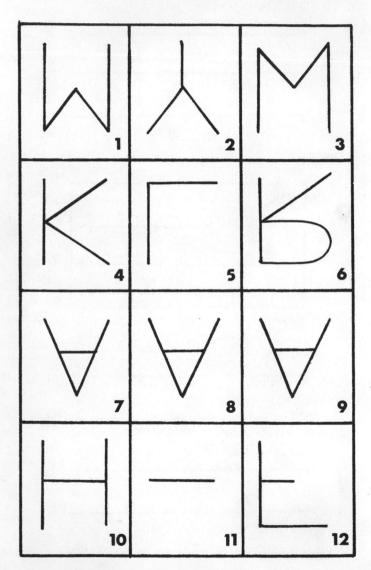

48

You'll have to do more to these twelve squares on the opposite page than put them in the right order to find out where you are now.

53. Wedding Belles

Hester, Heather and Hilary were three of the loveliest girls you could ever hope to meet. Hester was seventeen (and the winner of the "Miss Panty Hose" contest at Butlin's Department Store last year), Heather was eighteen (and the winner of the "Miss Ship-Shape" contest at the Navy Yard two years ago), and Hilary was nineteen (and the winner of the "Miss Whipped Butter" contest organized by the Milk Producers Council back in 1977). These three young beauties were engaged to be married, but the weddings never took place because the girls couldn't agree on who was going to marry whom.

They knew five things:

That HERBERT was a vet.
That HEATHER was not engaged to the accountant.
That the bank manager's future wife was not HILARY.
That HUBERT was engaged to HESTER.
That HORACE was an accountant.

But even knowing those five things, they couldn't work out who should have married whom. They had beauty, but no brains. Since you've got brains *and* beauty, can you say who should have married whom?

54. More Than Meets the Eye

How many triangles can you find in this diagram?

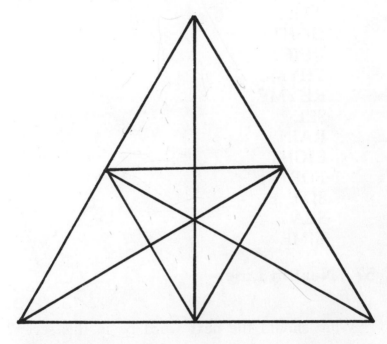

The answer's quite surprising, so keep counting.

55. Any Old Iron

Which is the heavier:
    a pound of feathers
    or a pound of iron?

56. Misplaced

Which of the words in this list does not belong?

FOUR
ATE
SIGHT
REIGN
THYME
RHYME
SEE
RAIN
EIGHT
FOR
SITE
SEA
TIME

57. Next in Line

What should the next word be in this series?

AARDWOLF
ABANDON
ACCLAIM
ADDITION
AEROPLANE
AFTERNOON
AGE
?

58. Tall Story

Which of these two blocks is the taller?

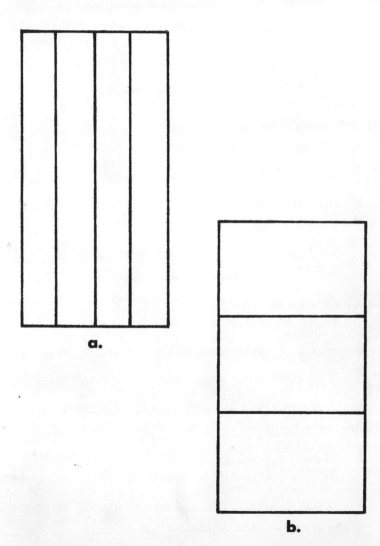

a.

b.

59. Plus Plus Equals Equals

An automobile + a domestic animal = something you walk over. Get it? An automobile (Car) + a domestic animal (Pet) = something you walk over (Carpet). It's easy really—once you know how.

Well, now you know how, give these a try. They won't bend your mind, but they'll tease your brain.

1. Salt water + a daughter's brother = a time of year = ...

2. In the middle + the present tense of "got" = a very small person = ...

3. A nickname for sailor + allow = something to drink from = ...

4. Stout + that woman = a parent = ...

5. The past of sit + a vase = a planet = ...

6. A young dog + a domestic animal = a doll on strings = ...

7. What a foot is attached to + something final = a mythical story = ...

8. What a shark has + what people drink = the end of the show = ...

9. What pigs give us + allow = a small village
   = ...

10. An automobile + decay = a vegetable
    = ...

11. The opposite of women + the highest card
    = something sinister = ...

12. The opposite of on + something frozen =
    a place to work = ...

13. A fiend + what you breathe = to harm
    = ...

14. What campers sleep on + 2,000 pounds =
    a kind of material = ...

15. What you wear on your head + a color =
    great dislike = ...

16. What beggars do + what comes before two
    = get away! = ...

17. A Mafia chieftain + what opens a door =
    an ass = ...

18. A chum + the highest card = where the
    Queen lives = ...

19. What you do with needle and thread + how
    old you are = what sewers carry = ...

20. To put down + where golfers start = a sofa
    = ...

60. Disunited

In this list, can you spot the odd man out?

T O B S N O
C C A O G H I
P P H H I I A A L L E D
F R A N C O C I S S A N
O R W N E N S L A E
N A I A I L C O R F

61. Uncommon in Common

What do these two words have in common?

ABSTEMIOUS
FACETIOUS

And what do they mean?

62. One to Eight

Take the eight digits from one to eight:

1
2
3
4
5
6
7
8

And put each one of them in a different box in this diagram:

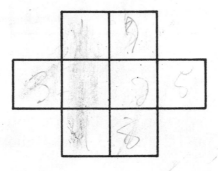

There's a catch to it, of course. No two numbers that follow one another must go in a box beside each other.

	1	2	
3	4	5	6
	7	8	

This is wrong, because you can't have 1 next to 2, 3 next to 4, 4 next to 5, 5 next to 6 and 6 next to 7.

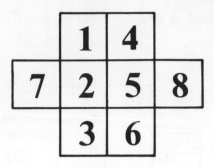

And this is wrong too, because you can't have 1 above 2, and 2 above 3, and 4 above 5 and 5 above 6.

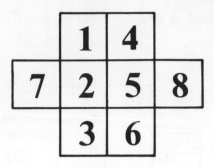

And this is wrong as well, because the box with 1 touches the box with 2, and the box with 3 touches the box with 4, and the box with 5 touches the box with 6 and the box with 7 touches the box with 8.

So, if no two consecutive numbers can go side by side—either horizontally or vertically or diagonally—how are you going to fit the eight digits, 1, 2, 3, 4, 5, 6, 7 and 8, into the diagram?

63. Fooled Ya!

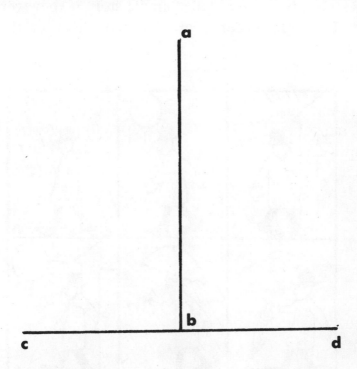

Which of these two lines is the longer? Is it the vertical line from a to b? Or the horizontal line from c to d?

And don't you dare use a ruler. That's cheating!

64. Simple Story

Here are nine pictures that tell a simple story. Rather, they *would* tell a simple story if they were in the right order. Can you put them in that order?

65. The Mirkle Museum

Professor Miles Mirkle was a fraud and his museum in Mudville was filled with phony exhibits. There were a few genuine items on display, of course, but most of the pieces in the Mirkle Museum were very far from being authentic. Here are some of the exhibits that Professor Mirkle listed in his catalogue. Can you spot the phonies?

1. A photograph of Abraham Lincoln.
2. A deck of playing cards used in 1700.
3. A pipe smoked by William the Conqueror.
4. An 1815 postage stamp.
5. The knife used to assassinate President McKinley.
6. Christopher Columbus's wristwatch.
7. Benjamin Franklin's pocket handkerchief.
8. The uniform worn by General Custer at the Battle of the Bulge.
9. Winston Churchill's dress wig.
10. A 1750 United States dollar bill.
11. The uniform of the captain of the *S.S. Titanic*.
12. Mark Twain's manuscript of *Wuthering Heights*.

U. S.
ONE DOLLAR BILL
1750

13. A soup bowl used by Thomas Jefferson.
14. Souvenirs of the Presidential election campaign of Andrew Johnson.
15. Martha Washington's silver thimble.

66. Flower Power

S O R E
R I I S
S A P Y N
K A O
C U B P T U R T E
C R I D H O

Which of these words doesn't belong to the series?

67. Love Story

Andy was in love. He was very much in love and the girl he was in love with was none other than dear, sweet, lovable Lulu. Andy spent his days thinking about Lulu and his nights dreaming about her. He adored her. He loved her so much that he wanted to marry her and make her Mrs. Andy.

Unfortunately for poor Andy, Lulu loved another. She *liked* Andy, of course, liked him very much, in fact, but she didn't love him and was sure she never could. Lulu loved Teddy. And because she loved Teddy she found Andy a nuisance. Every day he would call on her and expect her to give him a cup of tea and a kiss and a hug. He only got the cup of tea, but he never gave up hoping for the kiss and the hug.

One day Lulu felt she had had just about enough of Andy. She couldn't stand his company a minute longer and to show him how fed up she was she took out a piece of paper and drew eight circles on it, like this:

She then said to Andy, "Andy, have you ever heard the secret of the eight O's?"

"No, Lulu darling, I haven't," Andy replied.

"Well, let me show you then," said she, and she added four vertical lines to the eight circles.

Andy looked at the piece of paper and blushed. He left Lulu there and then and never ever bothered her again.

What difference did the four vertical lines make to the eight O's?

68. Lewis Carroll's Brain-Teaser

Lewis Carroll, the clergyman and mathematician whose real name was Charles Dodgson, didn't create just Alice in Wonderland, you know. He also created all sorts of mind-bending brain-teasers and this is one of his favorites:

64

"I have two clocks.

One of them has stopped completely. The other one gains half a minute every twenty-four hours.

Which of the two clocks tells the exact time more often?"

.Well?

69. The Brain-Twisting Twist

A hundred years ago there lived a wise and wonderful German mathematician called Ferdinand Mobius. Not only was he wise and wonderful, he was also the inventor of something that has come to be called the Mobius Strip.

To find out more about this mind-boggling invention of his, you must make one for yourself. It's very easy. All you need is a strip of newspaper that's a couple of inches wide and about two feet long. Give the strip of paper one twist and then glue the ends together. You've created a Mobius Strip all of your own.

What's remarkable about this strip is that you'll find it only has one surface. A normal loop of paper would have two surfaces: the inside and the outside. The Mobius Strip has only one and you can check this for yourself by taking a pencil and drawing a line along the strip. You won't need to remove the pencil from the paper, but the line you draw will eventually meet itself and you will have covered the entire strip with one line.

A pair of scissors will help you discover something even more extraordinary about the Mobius Strip. If you cut an ordinary loop down the middle, you will produce two separate loops. If you cut a Mobius Strip down the middle, you will simply produce one giant loop, twice the size of the loop you started with and now containing two twists in it instead of one.

What's more, if you take your scissors to this new, larger loop and cut it a third of the width from the edge and keep cutting until it meets up with itself, you will eventually produce two interlocking loops, the larger one containing two twists in it and the smaller containing just one!

Who would have thought that so much could be done with a simple strip of
paper and a simple
single twist?

70. Pattern Power

The four patterns in these four squares have something in common. What is it?

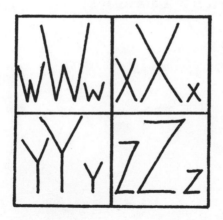

Once you've worked out what it is, you'll have no difficulty discovering which one of the six patterns in the squares opposite belongs to the set of four above.

71. The Same Only Different

Here are six ordinary English words:

CALMNESS
CANOPY
DEFT
FIRST
SIGHING
STUN

What do they have in common?

72. Tricky Triangles

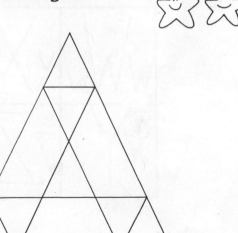

How many triangles can you count in the drawing?

73. The Nelson Touch

Admiral Lord Nelson is standing on top of his column in the middle of Trafalgar Square in London facing due West.

Given the instructions:

RIGHT TURN!
ABOUT TURN!
LEFT TURN!

which way would he end up facing?

74. Charles Dodgson's Brain-Teaser

Here is another favorite brain-teasing mind-bender by Charles Dodgson, whose pen name was Lewis Carroll.

> "I have a Russian friend who has three sons.
> The first son was called Rab and became a lawyer.
> The second son was called Ymra and became a soldier.
> The third son became a sailor. What was he called?"

Well?

75. Oddition

Write down five odd numbers so that when you add them up they total 14.

76. Albert's Alibi

At last, Detective Plod, Head of the New York Flying Squad, had got his man. Albert Albert was the cruel swine who had poisoned the Yorkies on Staten Island. After a hunt that went on for many months, Plod had caught up with the criminal and arrested him. Now Plod had brought Albert back to headquarters for questioning.

"What were you doing on the night of August 3rd?" thundered Plod.

"Well, sir," Albert Albert replied, "I was nowhere near Staten Island, that's for sure. If you want to know, I had gone to Washington for the day to visit my maiden aunt. She's a sweet old lady and because she lives on her own she gets a little lonely and always welcomes a little company. I'm her only surviving cousin you see, and we're very fond of each other. Anyway, I'll never forget the day because of the terrible journey. I'd arrived at Grand Central Station in good time and bought my ticket. It cost $3. I remember that very clearly because I gave the man a $3 bill and I didn't get any change. Well, once the bus got started I settled back to enjoy the flight. But no sooner had we left San Francisco, than the bus skidded to a halt. Apparently, there was ice on the road. Anyway, the driver did his best to navigate the road and eventually we got going again. We set off at 9:00 a.m. and didn't reach our destination until nearly noon and, believe you me, I was very glad to get off the bus and stretch my legs after six hours traveling. I managed to find a taxi right outside the station and took it all the way to my aunt's house on the outskirts of the city. When I arrived she and her brother Ted were so pleased to see me. It was her 30th birthday, after all, and I had brought her a lovely bunch of spring flowers. After we'd all given each other a big kiss, we sat down with the Monopoly board and played Bridge all evening. And if you don't believe me, you can check it all out with her. Her name is Mrs. Spriggs and her address is Apt. 12E, 999 State St., Washington, D.C."

"Albert Albert," roared Plod, "your whole story is a pack of lies."

The detective was quite right, of course, but how many of Albert Albert's lies did you spot?

77. Sweet Sum

At Sweeney's Sweet Shop in Swarthmore you can buy three lollipops and one gumdrop for the same price as two sticks of licorice. One lollipop, two gumdrops and three sticks of licorice will cost you a total of 50¢.

How much are lollipops, gumdrops and sticks of licorice at Sweeney's Sweet Shop in Swarthmore?

78. Tic-Tac-Toe

Jack and Lucy are playing Tic-Tac-Toe. Jack has X and Lucy has O.

O	X	O
1	**2**	**3**
X	**4**	**5**

Jack and Lucy have had two turns each.

If it's now Jack's turn, where should he put his X to be sure of winning?

If it's now Lucy's turn, where should she put her O to be sure of winning?

79. Presidential Poser

The Constitution of the United States of America specifies four basic requirements for becoming President:

1. The candidate must be at least thirty-five years of age.
2. The candidate must have been born an American citizen in the United States.
3. The candidate must have lived in the United States for at least fourteen years.

What is the fourth requirement?

80. Weird Words

Here are some familiar and some not-so-familiar words:

BRANDY
CRATERS
PIRATED
SCAMPI
WRINGS
TRAMPS
STORES

What do they all have in common?

81. Clock Watching

If you follow the sequence in the first five clocks, what time should the sixth clock give?

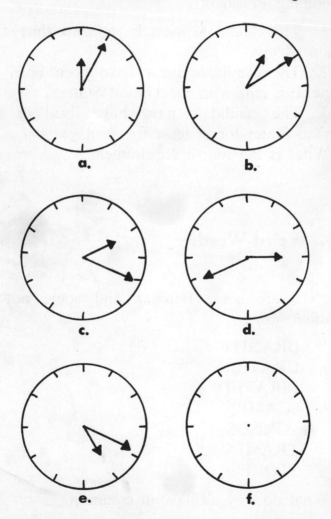

a.

b.

c.

d.

e.

f.

82. Zoo Time

A clutch of kangaroos and a bevy of bison had 86 heads and 240 feet between them.

How many kangaroos were there?
And how many bison?

83. The Poet's Puzzle

What is the beginning of eternity,
The end of time and space,
The beginning of every end,
And the end of every race?

84. Twelve Letter Teaser

There is a twelve-letter word that not every-body knows that the dictionary says means "charming . . . agreeable . . . meant to gain favor with someone."

You've got to find that word. Its first three letters are exactly the same as its last three letters, and these are the six letters that fall in between:

———R A T I A T———

85. Cleo and Boa

You know, of course, that Boadicea died 129 years after Cleopatra was born.

(You didn't know that? Shame on you!)

You know too, of course, that if you combined their ages you will find that between them they lived for 100 years.

(You didn't know that either? Really! Where did you go to school?)

Finally, you know, of course, that Cleopatra died in the year 30 B.C.

(And you mean to say you didn't even know that! Disgraceful!)

Well, given all you know, can you say when Boadicea was born?

86. The Wooden Triangle

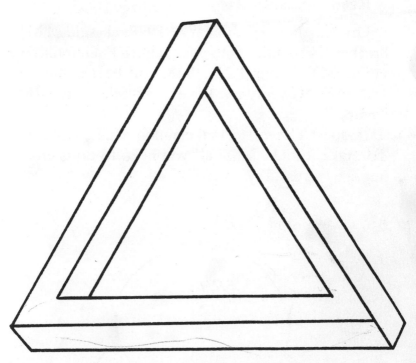

If you really enjoy teasing your brain, why not take up woodwork and begin your career as a craftsman by building a model of this wooden triangle?

If ever there was a mind-bender that really bent minds, this is it!

87. Confusion!

Read this sentence:

On the first of January, 1977, I said, "My brother Benjamin who was (born) (baptized) (married) on April 22, 1958, will be (eighteen) (twenty) (twenty-one) next (week) (month) (year)."

It doesn't seem to make much sense, does it? To make it make sense all you need to do is cross out six words. Try.

88. Join the Dots

There are twelve dots marked around this circle. Some of them are already joined to each other by straight lines.

In all, how many straight lines would be needed to join every dot to every other dot?

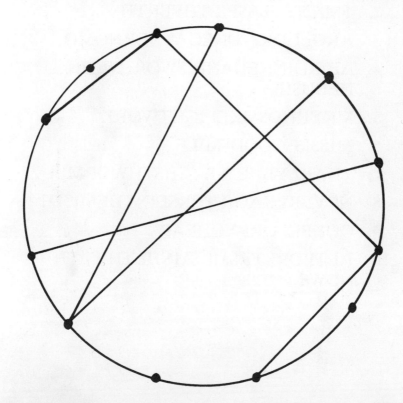

89. Look for the Letter

If you can uncover the missing letters in each of these sentences you'll be very much the wiser, because they're not just any old sentences picked at random from out of a hat—they're familiar proverbs.

1. ASTTCHNTMESAVESNNE

2. TMANYCKSSPILTHEBRTH

3. AROLLINGTONEGATHERNOMO

4. ABIRDINHEHANDISWORHWOIN HEBUSH

5. MNYHNDSMKELIGHTWORK

6. MISSISSGOODSMILE

7. THARLYBIRDCATCHSTHWORM

8. NEVERLKAGIFTHRSEINTHEMUTH

9. OOKBEFOREYOUEAP

10. RLTBDRLTRSMKSMNHLTHWLTH NDWS

90. Poetic Poser

Here's a little verse that tells a sad tale:

Twice four and twenty blackbirds
Were sitting in the rain;
I shot and killed a sixth part—
How many did remain?

And don't rush in with your answer. Read the verse twice more before you try to solve this teasing teaser.

91. Piggy in the Corner

A 6-sided pig sty had a pig in each corner, five pigs ahead of each pig and a pig on each pig's tail. How many pigs were there in the pig sty?

92. Calendar Counter

This brain-teaser has to do with dates and days and if you have a calendar at hand you'll find it that much easier to answer. Try it:

When the day before yesterday was referred to as "the day after tomorrow,"
    the day that was then called "yesterday"
        was as far away from the day we now call "tomorrow"
        as yesterday is from the day on which we shall now be able to speak of last Monday as
        "a week ago yesterday!"

What day is it?

93. Six Words

These six words have something in common:

    Seperate
    Embarassed
    Adress
    Wierd
    Resteraunt
    Untill

What is it?

94. The Amazing Brick

This isn't a puzzle, though it's puzzling all right. Just take a good look at this brick. Now close your eyes. Open them and take another good look.

The brick appears to change its position, doesn't it? Sometimes you feel you are looking at it from above. Sometimes you feel you are looking at it from below. And if you stare at it long enough, it'll seem to change before your very eyes!

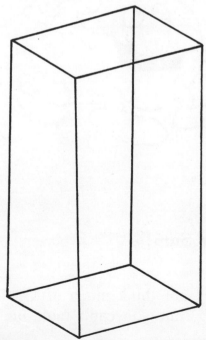

95. Animal Crackers

Can you name the well-known animal which at first walks on four legs, later walks on two and later still walks on three?

The answer, you'll be surprised to learn, is closer to you than you think.

96. Some Sum!

You may not think much of Uncle Herbert's handwriting, but you can't fault his arithmetic, can you?

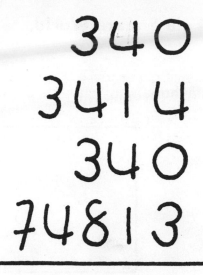

$$
\begin{array}{r}
340 \\
3414 \\
340 \\
74813 \\
\hline
43373414 \\
\hline
\end{array}
$$

Oh, so the sum doesn't seem to add up to you. That's odd, because it adds up to Uncle Herbert. Think about it for a moment more and see if you can't make some sense out of the sum.

97. It's a Square World

In all, how many squares do you see here?

One, you say. Quite right.

In all, how many squares do you see here?

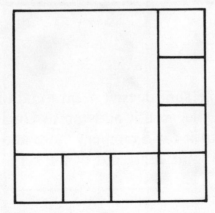

Nine, you say. Quite right.

Since you can count, in all how many squares can you see here?

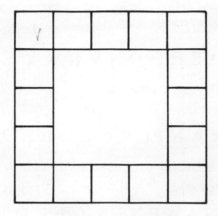

And how many squares can you see here?

98. Make Your Own Arrangements

Rearrange this series of letters to form an everyday word:

A A E E D D N V R W Y Y O R

Now rearrange this series of letters to form an irregular verb:

V R A N I E R G E U B R R A L

Now rearrange this series of letters to form a slang expression:

S S S A A P N N L G E E O I X R

Finally rearrange this series of letters to form a month of the year:

F R E A M O T Y O H E N A H T

99. Brotherly Love

A great surgeon had a brother who died.
The man who died didn't have a brother.
So how were the great surgeon and the man who died related?

100. Jock the Doc

Old Doctor Jock McSporran is the oldest teacher at Saint Andrew's University, which is the oldest university in Scotland. He was born in 1879 and he has been teaching Scripture at Saint Andrew's for seventy-five years. He says he has lived so long because of his excellent diet: a bowl

of porridge and a bottle of the water from Loch Ness taken twice daily. He says he knows so much because he's got a good memory and the finest library in all Scotland.

It is indeed a very wonderful library, full of truly remarkable books (including this one), but what is curious about the books is that no two of them contain the same number of words. The number of books in the library is greater than the number of words in the largest book in the library.

Well, now you know all that, you'll be able to answer Doctor Jock McSporran's favorite question about his library: "How many words does one of the books contain and what is the book about?"

101. Ancient Teaser

Here's a teaser that's so old it's grown white whiskers. In fact, it was old when Doctor Jock McSporran was a boy. When he first heard it, in the summer of 1900, it took him three minutes to solve. See how long it takes you.

All you've got to do is make a sensible sentence out of this:

| stand | take | to | taking |
| I | you | throw | my |

102. Clowning Around

Here are six clowns:

Can you find the two pairs of clowns who match? Then can you find the two odd ones?

103. Jungle Story

Colonel Carter was lost. He was in the middle of the wildest part of Pogologoland. Pogologoland was lost in the heart of darkest South America, which was quite a problem for poor Colonel Carter, especially since the intrepid explorer spoke not a word of Pogologo. He knew that Pogo meant either "Yes" or "No," but he wasn't sure which. And he was certain that Logo meant either "No" or "Yes," but he wasn't sure which.

Colonel Carter stumbled through the undergrowth in growing desperation. Suddenly he came across a native. "This man will help me," thought Colonel Carter to himself. Certainly the native looked friendly enough. The trouble was, although he could understand a bit of English, he could only speak in Pogologo.

"Am I headed for safety?" asked Colonel Carter.

"Pogo!" came the quick reply.

But what did the native's answer mean? "Yes" or "No"? Colonel Carter spoke only four more words and got the answer he wanted.

What was Colonel Carter's second question?

104. Dots and Areas

1 dot
1 area

2 dots
2 areas

3 dots
4 areas

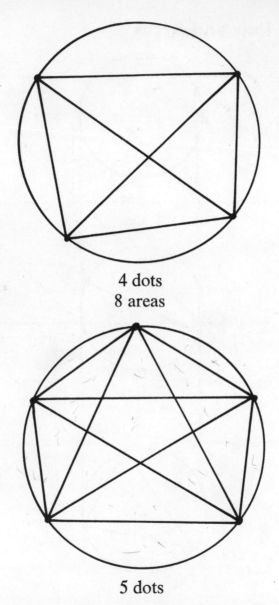

4 dots
8 areas

5 dots
—but how many areas this time?

105. Last Words

Take these twelve triangles and turn them into six squares—and what do you get?

ANSWERS

1. For Starters

The word "BRAIN-TEASER."

2. Twin Twister

Horace and Doris Norris are two children from a set of triplets. The third triplet was called Morris.

3. Letter Salad

I C A Z. The other letters read aloud all mean something (I see a sea, I see a bee, I see a jay, I see a ewe), but I C A Z means nothing.

4. Equal Division

The king said that one son should divide the property in half, and the other son should choose which half he wanted.

5. Please Translate

A nod is as good as a wink to a blind horse.

6. Ninety-Nine Not Out

66.

7. A Time Teaser

9:30

8. Odd Man Out

All the men with smiling faces have upturned feet and all the men with sad faces have down-turned feet, so Number 10 is the odd man out because he has a sad face and upturned feet.

9. Alarming

Only one hour and a quarter—because your alarm will have awakened you at 8:15 that night!

10. Scrambled Eggs

1. I prefer scrambled eggs to boiled eggs.
2. A brainy brain has no trouble with tough brain teasers.
3. Always brush your teeth twice a day if you want to avoid tooth decay.
4. The unicorn is a mythical beast and the dinosaur is extinct.

5. To say that five times five is fifty is to make a foolish mistake.
6. Chicago is known as the windy city.
7. John Glenn was not the first man on the moon.
8. A fool and his money are soon parted.
9. The aardvark is a small creature that is like a cross between an armadillo and an ant-eater.
10. All the world's a stage and the men and women merely players.

11. Surprise Your Eyes

Almost certainly you thought the central circle in figure 2 was the larger, but your eyes were deceiving you. Both the central circles are *exactly* the same size.

12. Sixty-Second Countdown

If you did it in a minute you're some kind of a math genius or you know the trick which makes this puzzle a snap! You add the first and last figures on the list (1 + 200). They total 201. Now take the next pair (2 + 199) which also totals 201, as does 3 + 198, 4 + 197, and so on down to the final pair, 100 + 101. Since it's obvious right away that each pair will total 201 and that you have 100 pairs, just multiply 201 by 100, for a total of 20,100.

13. The Missing Letter

Q

14. What's What?

1. A bald head.
2. Tomorrow.
3. Your breath.
4. A pack of cards.
5. The letter E.
6. A sponge.
7. Silence.
8. Your future.
9. Snow.
10. A hole.
11. A pen.
12. A coffin.
13. Their own nose.
14. A right angle.
15. A candle.
16. A kiss.
17. A carpet.

18. Down—like swan's down.
19. The railroad track.
20. Holes.

15. Santa's Socks

  3.
19.

16. Next Number, Please

1. 31: the numbers are those of the days in the month, starting with January.
2. 48: the number doubles each time.
3. 0: the numbers represent the 20th century which began on January 1, 1901 and will end on December 31, 2000.
4. 65: each time you double the previous number and then subtract one.
5. 9: each time two numbers are followed by a third which is the figure you get when the two numbers are multiplied together.
6. 1: the figures represent the number of times a clock will strike if it strikes once every half-hour as well as striking on the hour; the series here begins at 11:30.

7. 9: 1(+5=) 6, 2(+5=) 7, 3(+5=) 8, 4(+5=) 9.
8. 536: you must subtract 101 each time.
9. 8589934592: each number is multiplied by half of itself to form the next number.
10. 250: it's simply 1000 divided first by 9, then by 8, then by 7, then by 6, then by 5, then by 4.

17. Looking Ahead

1992

18. One Word

NOON.

19. Spooner's Spoonerisms

1. If you don't hurry you will miss the last bus.
2. I have just received a crushing blow.
3. Who killed Cock Robin?
4. There's nothing like a good lunch of eggs and hash.
5. What shall we do with a drunken sailor?

6. Who kissed my mate Kate is still a mystery.
7. The little dog laughed to see such fun and the cow jumped over the moon.
8. We wish you a Merry Christmas and a Happy New Year.
9. It's dark in the park after six at night.
10. This is a silly party game if ever I played one.

20. Ling Ting Wan Faw Su

He was a midget and could only reach as high as the button for the nineteenth floor when he was in the elevator.

21. Tall Tale

They're all the same height!

22. All the Signs

Square 7 is the odd one because in all the others the plus sign faces the minus sign and the multiplication sign faces the division sign.

23. Crazy Quiz

1. Albumen. If you put yolk, you spelled the yellow of an egg!
2. One.
3. A 50¢ piece and a quarter. One of them wasn't a quarter, but the other one was!
4. The letter A.
5. Incorrectly.
6. All twelve.
7. 202 each time!
8. 12, of course!
9. January 1st and December 31st fall in the same year every year.
10. Probably!

24. One Number

1.

25. Unlucky Thirteen

R. All the others are the initial letters of the twelve months of the year.

26. Loony Letters

1. Because it comes right in the middle of day.

2. E.
3. They become C-sick.
4. Because "we" cannot be "wed" without it.
5. Because it comes at the end of life.
6. Because it is the capital of France.
7. Because it comes in the middle of night.
8. Because it makes the "ear" "hear."
9. Because it means the end of ski.
10. Because it is a jay.
11. Because it comes at the end of pork.
12. Because it makes an "imp" "limp."
13. Because you don't want to make mice out of "ice."
14. Because it makes "a sty" "nasty."
15. Because it is always in order.
16. Because it will make an "ass" "pass."
17. Because it is seldom seen without U.
18. Because they'd be "fiends" without it.
19. Because it makes the "cream" "scream."
20. Because it comes at the end of Lent.
21. Because it's always in the center of fun.
22. Because it comes between two eyes.
23. Because it always makes "ink" "wink."
24. Because it is never in "good health."
25. Because it makes "Pa" "pay."
26. Because it comes at the end of the alphabet.

27. Wonder Word

Rhythm.

28. Homeroom 102

The boys must have at least 3 pennies each to start with, so they will have enough to give 1 penny to each girl. Each girl will get at least 3 pennies, and must then have at least 9 pennies, so she will have enough to give an equal number to each boy. Each girl can't have just 6 pennies to start, though, because then she would have to give 1 back to each boy and have none for herself, leaving them unequal. If the girls start out with 15, they can take 1 penny from each boy (leaving each boy with no pennies, each girl with 18). The girls can then give each boy 1 penny, leaving themselves with 1 penny as well.

29. Two to Go

C H. It's the word ARCHITECT spelled forward and backwards.

30. Card Sharp

The Ten of diamonds, the King of hearts, the Eight of spades.

31. The Longest Line

All three lines are exactly equal in length.

32. Cats Catch Rats

5.

33. The Two Bricklayers

Husband and wife.

34. Triangular Challenge

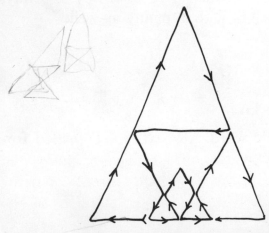

35. Seven Numbers

60. It's the only one of the numbers that isn't divisible by 7.

36. The Longer Line

Both lines are exactly equal in length.

37. New Haven Bound

Exactly where he jumped!

38. What's Missing?

39. What Comes Next?

1000. The figures show the denominations of bills and notes in the American currency, starting with the dollar bill and going through to the $1000 bill.

40. What's This?

It's all the letters of the alphabet that are made up of straight lines when written as capitals, but with one line missed out of each letter.

41. Family Reunion

Two sisters and their brother, their father and mother and their two paternal grandparents.

42. Ask a Silly Question

1. A toothbrush, a comb and an umbrella—of course!
2. Your lap.
3. Your temper.
4. The letter M.
5. A mirror.
6. The letter G.
7. A broken drum.
8. Chili sauce.
9. The nose.
10. A towel.
11. A promise.

43. What's Next?

1. U. These are all the letters of the alphabet that contain curves.
2. U. This is a list of every other letter in the alphabet.
3. Y. These are the initial letters of the words of *Baa Baa Black Sheep Have You Any Wool?*
4. T. These letters form the words "THE ALPHABET" in reverse.
5. Z. AB, three letters are missed, FG, three letters are missed, KL, three letters are missed, and so on, right through to Z.
6. P. The letters are the next 3 letters that follow each of the five vowels.
7. S. These are the initial letters of the words of *Three Blind Mice.*
8. G. This is a list of every third letter in the alphabet (repeated).
9. R. As in GYLES BRANDRETH!

44. Think Big

1. As large as the moon.
2. From the Earth to Mars and back again three times.
3. As high as a mountain.

45. Pick a Pint

First, fill the three-pint jug; then empty the water from the three-pint jug into the five-pint jug; then fill the three-pint jug again. Now empty as much as you can from the three-pint jug into the five-pint jug and when the five-pint jug is full you will find that what's left in the three-pint jug is just one pint.

46. Lost Letter

L. Starting with J, you take the letter before it, then the letter after it, then the letter but one before it, then the letter but one after it, and so on.

47. Dotty

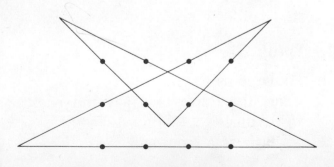

48. A Comedy of Errors

The first mistake is the spelling of "Their," which should be "There."

The second mistake is the spelling of "misteaks," which should be "mistakes."

The third mistake is that the sentence only contains *two* mistakes.

49. Poor Miss Gump

Because if Miss Gump knew that the third letter was an R, she didn't need to know for what it stood.

50. Nutty Numbers

1. Because two times ten is twenty and two times eleven is twenty-two (twenty, too)!
2. Nine.
3. Seven (s/even).
4. Because it is too (two) gross! (A gross is twelve dozen things.)
5. 8.
6. Zero!
7. Only once: any subsequent subtractions will be from a smaller number.
8. You must bring him 2!

9. When they make 11.
10. Six dozen dozen is 864 and a half dozen dozen is 72, so the difference between them is 792.

51. A Problem of Parallels

Despite appearances, all twelve lines on the page are parallel.

52. Where Are We Now?

If you turn the squares inside out and upside down and then arrange them in this order—10, 7, 5, 12, 11, 3, 8, 2, 1, 9, 6, 4—you will find that you've reached the *Half-Way Mark*. With about half the brain-teasers and mind-benders gone and about half still to come what else would you expect?

53. Wedding Belles

Hester and Hubert.
Hilary and Horace.
Heather and Herbert.

54. More Than Meets the Eye

At least 47.

55. Any Old Iron

They both weigh the same, of course—a pound.

56. Misplaced

RHYME. All the other words can be paired off into homonyms (that means words that sound the same, but have different meanings).

57. Next in Line

AHEAD or AHOY or any other word beginning with the letters AH. In the list all the words begin with A and the second letters run through the alphabet from B to C to D to E and so on.

58. Tall Story

Both blocks are exactly the same size.

59. Plus Plus Equals Equals

1. Season.
2. Midget.
3. Goblet.
4. Father.
5. Saturn.
6. Puppet.
7. Legend.
8. Finale.
9. Hamlet.
10. Carrot.
11. Menace.
12. Office.
13. Impair.
14. Cotton.
15. Hatred.
16. Begone.
17. Donkey.
18. Palace.
19. Sewage.
20. Settee.

60. Disunited

Five of the six sets of letters are the jumbled-up names of cities: BOSTON, CHICAGO, PHILADELPHIA, SAN FRANCISCO and NEW ORLEANS. The sixth set of letters is the jumbled-up version of CALIFORNIA which is the odd man out because it's a state, not a city.

61. Uncommon in Common

Both the words contain the five vowels once and once only and in their correct alphabetical order. ABSTEMIOUS means "sparing, not greedy or self-indulgent." FACETIOUS means "being full of witticisms and wise-cracks."

62. One to Eight

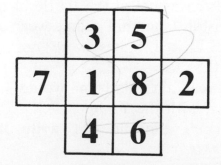

63. Fooled Ya!

Surprisingly, the horizontal line from c to d is actually a quarter of an inch *longer* than the vertical line from a to b. And now you're allowed to use your ruler to check.

64. Simple Story

6, 2, 8, 3, 9, 1, 7, 5, 4.

65. The Mirkle Museum

3. There was no tobacco in the time of William the Conqueror.
4. There were no postage stamps in 1815.
5. President McKinley was shot.
6. Wristwatches didn't exist in Christopher Columbus's day.
8. Custer was not at the Battle of the Bulge.
9. Winston Churchill didn't wear a wig.
10. The United States were not united in 1750.
11. The captain's uniform would have gone down with the *Titanic*.
12. Mark Twain did not write *Wuthering Heights*.

14. Andrew Johnson was never elected President.

All the other items listed are perfectly possible.

66. Flower Power

The letters are jumbled-up versions of the words ROSE, IRIS, PANSY, OAK, BUTTER-CUP, and ORCHID. OAK is obviously the oddball since it is a tree and the others are all flowers.

67. Love Story

68. Lewis Carroll's Brain-Teaser

The clock that gains half a minute every twenty-four hours will only tell the exact time every 1440 days, while the clock that has stopped completely will show the exact time twice daily, because in order for the first clock to tell the exact time it will have to gain 12 hours (720 minutes) which at the rate of half a minute per day will take 1440 (2 × 720) days.

70. Pattern Power

What the four patterns have in common is this: the largest letter is in the center, the second largest is on the left, the smallest is on the right. This means that the pattern in square 3 matches the set of four.

71. The Same Only Different

Each of the six words contains three letters of the alphabet in their consecutive alphabetical order: LMN, NOP, DEF, RST, GHI, STU.

72. Tricky Triangles

14.

73. The Nelson Touch

East.

74. Charles Dodgson's Brain-Teaser

Yvan. The lawyer's name is "bar" spelled backwards, the soldier's name is "army" spelled backwards, so the sailor's name is "navy" spelled backwards.

75. Oddition

```
   11
    1
    1
+   1
─────
   14
```

76. Albert's Alibi

1. Albert is his aunt's nephew, not her cousin.
2. To get to Washington from New York costs more than $3 and there is no such thing as a $3 bill.
3. To catch a bus Albert wouldn't have gone to Grand Central Station.
4. On a bus you wouldn't enjoy "the flight."
5. How has Albert suddenly gotten to San Francisco from Grand Central Station?
6. It's unlikely that there would have been ice on the line in August.

7. If the journey lasted from 9:00 a.m. until nearly noon, Albert was not traveling for six hours.
8. Why did the aunt have a brother with her if she lived alone and was known to be lonely?
9. If she was 30 she couldn't also have been "a sweet old lady."
10. You don't normally find spring flowers in August.
11. You don't play Bridge with a Monopoly board. You play Bridge with cards.
12. If she was a "maiden aunt" she wouldn't be called *Mrs.* Spriggs.
13. If she lived in a house her address wouldn't be Apt. 12E.

77. Sweet Sum

4¢, 8¢ and 10¢.

78. Tic-Tac-Toe

Jack should put his X in square 4.
Lucy should put her O in square 5.

79. Presidential Poser

4. The candidate must be elected!

80. Weird Words

Each of the words can be reduced by one letter at a time and still remain full words:

BRANDY, BRAND, BRAN, RAN, AN, A.

CRATERS, CRATER, CRATE, RATE, RAT, AT, A.

PIRATED, PIRATE, IRATE, RATE, ATE, AT, A.

SCAMPI, SCAMP, CAMP, CAM, AM, A.

WRINGS, WINGS, WING, WIN, IN, I.

TRAMPS, TRAMP, RAMP, RAM, AM, A.

STORES, STORE, TORE, ORE, OR, O.

81. Clock Watching

Each clock is advanced by one hour plus double the minutes shown on the previous clock, so 12:05 leads to 1 + 10 (1:10), 1:10 leads to 2 + 20 (2:20), 2:20 leads to 3 + 40 (3:40), 3:40 leads to 4 + 80 (5:20), 5:20 leads to 6 + 40 (6:40).

82. Zoo Time

52 kangaroos and 34 bison.

83. The Poet's Puzzle

The letter E.

84. Twelve Letter Teaser

INGRATIATING

85. Cleo and Boa

1 B.C.

86. The Wooden Triangle

You're right! It's an impossible triangle!

87. Confusion!

On the first of January, 1977, I said, "My brother Ben, who was born on April 22, 1958, will be twenty next year."

88. Join the Dots

66 lines.

89. Look for the Letter

1. I. A STITCH IN TIME SAVES NINE.
2. O. TOO MANY COOKS SPOIL THE BROTH.
3. S. A ROLLING STONE GATHERS NO MOSS.

4. T. A BIRD IN THE HAND IS WORTH TWO IN THE BUSH.
5. A. MANY HANDS MAKE LIGHT WORK.
6. A. A MISS IS AS GOOD AS A MILE.
7. E. THE EARLY BIRD CATCHES THE WORM.
8. O. NEVER LOOK A GIFT HORSE IN THE MOUTH.
9. L. LOOK BEFORE YOU LEAP.
10. A, E, I, O, U and Y. EARLY TO BED, EARLY TO RISE, MAKES A MAN HEALTHY, WEALTHY AND WISE.

90. Poetic Poser

Twice four and twenty is 48. Eight of these (a sixth part) are the ones that remained because they are dead. All the others flew off when the shots were fired.

91. Piggy in the Corner

Six.

92. Calendar Counter

Thursday.

93. Six Words

All six words are spelled incorrectly. This is how they should be spelled: separate, embarrassed, address, weird, restaurant, until.

94. The Amazing Brick

95. Animal Crackers

The human animal, which crawls on all fours as a baby, walks on two legs as an adult and has the third leg of a walking stick when old!

96. Some Sum!

Simply turn the page upside down and you will find the sum adds up all right!

97. It's a Square World

22 squares.
46 squares.

98. Make Your Own Arrangements

AN EVERYDAY WORD, AN IRREGULAR VERB, A SLANG EXPRESSION, A MONTH OF THE YEAR.

99. Brotherly Love

They were sister and brother.

100. Jock the Doc

None. It's a book of blank pages about nothing.

101. Ancient Teaser

I understand you undertake to overthrow my undertaking.

102. Clowning Around

1 and 6, and 2 and 4 are the matching faces. 3 and 5 don't match.

103. Jungle Story

"Did you say Pogo?" Whatever the native now replies will be the word meaning "Yes."

104. Dots and Areas

5 dots and 16 areas.

105. Last Words

THE END.

INDEX

R